Plot your way to Year 6 Maths success!

Investigations are a great way to challenge pupils and help them develop problem-solving skills, so we've devoted an entire book to them!

It's packed with twelve open-ended investigations to help pupils think creatively about a range of topics. By the end of the book, they'll have developed fantastic reasoning skills to help them master the Year 6 curriculum.

We also have a matching Teacher Book that's full of helpful teaching guidance for every investigation. Enjoy!

What CGP is all about

Our sole aim here at CGP is to produce the highest quality books — carefully written, immaculately presented and dangerously close to being funny.

Then we work our socks off to get them out to you — at the cheapest possible prices.

Contents

Published by CGP

ISBN: 978 1 78908 898 4

Written by Amanda MacNaughton and Mike Ollerton.

Editors: Ellen Burton, Sharon Keeley-Holden, Sam Norman
Reviewer: Clare Selway
With thanks to Glenn Rogers and Caley Simpson for the proofreading.

Printed by Elanders Ltd, Newcastle upon Tyne.
Clipart from Corel®
Based on the classic CGP style created by Richard Parsons.

How to be a Maths Investigator

This book is packed with Maths Investigations, and there are some <u>special skills</u> that you'll need if you want to get to the bottom of them.

What you need to do is...

- Work systematically
- Spot patterns, make predictions and generate rules
- Show your thinking

Once you've got the hang of these <u>three easy steps</u>, you'll be <u>thinking like a real mathematician</u>. Not only that — these skills can help in lots of your <u>other school work</u> too.

1. Work Systematically

Working **SYSTEM**atically means that you have to have a... yep, a **SYSTEM** in place.
You'll often need to think about the <u>order</u> in which you do things.

Here's an example:

Imagine that a football team is designing a new kit.
How many different football kits could they create using just the items below?

You could just start randomly matching shirts and shorts... but that isn't working systematically. You need to have a system to make sure you have definitely recorded all the possible combinations.

If you want to work systematically, the first step would be to <u>choose one colour of shirt</u> and put it with each possible colour of shorts.

The next step would be to <u>do the same again for the next colour of shirt</u>.

And finally do the same again for the <u>last shirt colour</u>.

By being <u>systematic</u>, you <u>know</u> you have <u>every possible combination</u>.
There are <u>9</u> possible different football kits.

How to be a Maths Investigator

2. Spot Patterns, Make Predictions and Generate Rules

It's always good to <u>spot patterns</u> in maths. It can help you to <u>predict</u> what will happen next...

It takes <u>two pegs</u> to hang <u>one</u> towel on a washing line and <u>three</u> pegs to hang <u>two</u> towels — like this:

How many pegs are needed for <u>three</u> and <u>four</u> towels?

First, you could draw a picture showing the number of pegs needed for 3 towels.

Then make a <u>table</u> showing what you know so far.

Number of towels	Number of pegs
1	2
2	3
3	4
4	?

This shows an orderly way of recording your findings and helps to <u>spot a pattern</u>: the number of <u>pegs</u> is always <u>one more than the number of towels</u>.

From this you can <u>predict</u> that <u>5 pegs</u> are needed for <u>4 towels</u>.

You can then draw the picture to <u>test</u> your prediction.

You can also <u>generate a rule</u> from this pattern.

"To find out how many pegs are needed, add one to the number of towels."

And if you want to be super-clever, you can write your rule <u>algebraically</u>.

$$P = T + 1$$

T = number of towels
P = number of pegs

3. Show Your Thinking

This means writing down your <u>thoughts</u> — e.g. what you've <u>noticed</u> and <u>how you've worked</u>.

Investigate what happens when you add together different numbers of <u>single-digit odd numbers</u>.

Let's say you work systematically and come up with this.

If you're asked to <u>Show Your Thinking</u>, you could write something like this.

1 + 3 = 4	1 + 3 + 5 = 9
1 + 5 = 6	1 + 3 + 7 = 11
1 + 7 = 8	1 + 3 + 9 = 13
1 + 9 = 10	1 + 5 + 7 = 13

I began using only 2 numbers and every time the answer was even. When I started using 3 numbers I noticed the answers were all odd. I was systematic by beginning with the lowest number and changing the number I added each time. Now I am going to see what happens when I add four single-digit odd numbers together. I predict the answers will be even.

This proves to people that you know <u>what</u> you're doing, and <u>why</u>.

Always, Sometimes or Never?

Warm Up Question

Imagine that some of the keys on a calculator do not work.
How can you make the numbers 1-20 using only the keys below?
Write down the keys you must press in the correct order to get each number.

① "Multiplying numbers produces a higher number."

Remember to give examples to back up what you say and to make it clearer.

Show your thinking

Is this statement <u>always</u> true, <u>sometimes</u> true or <u>never</u> true?
Explain your answer.

(2) For each calculation below, think about what the **missing number** might be and write down your suggestion. Then try it out on your **calculator**. If your number is not correct, **try again**.

a) 6 × ? = 3

b) 5 × ? = 1

c) 10 × ? = 4

d) 30 × ? = 3

e) 30 × ? = 12

f) 3 × ? = –6

g) 4 × ? = –12

h) 10 × ? = –3

i) 0.5 × ? = 0.25

j) 0.1 × ? = 0.01

> Trial and Improvement is when you begin with one number, try it out and adjust it until you get to the right answer.

Show your thinking

"Multiplying numbers produces a higher number."
Is there anything you would change or add to your original thinking?

3 Find as many <u>multiplications</u> as you can which have an answer with exactly <u>2 decimal places</u> which is <u>between 0 and 1</u>.

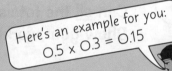

Here's an example for you:
0.5 × 0.3 = 0.15

You can't include 0.5 × 0.2 because the answer is 0.1, which only has 1 decimal place. Writing it as 0.10 isn't allowed!

Now Try This

$10 \times \_\_ = \_\_ \times 0.5$

There are two missing numbers in this equation. Each number can be whole, a decimal or a fraction, and positive or negative.
Investigate how many different ways you could complete this equation.

Section One — Calculations

Binary Numbers

Make the totals below by <u>adding</u>
numbers from the cards on the right.
You can only use each card <u>once</u> in a sum.

1) 9 ....

2) 14 ....

3) 21 ....

1   Can <u>all</u> the totals from 1 to 31 be made using the cards above?
Show your working.

31 is the biggest
number that can be
made with these cards.

2 The chart below shows how the numbers from 1 to 5 can be made using <u>binary column headings</u> and only the <u>digits 0 and 1</u>. Complete the table to show how the numbers 6 to 16 can be made.

16	8	4	2	1	
				1	= 1
			1	0	= 2
			1	1	= 3
		1	0	0	= 4
		1	0	1	= 5
					= 6
					= 7
					= 8
					= 9
					= 10
					= 11
					= 12
					= 13
					= 14
					= 15
					= 16

What <u>patterns</u> do you notice in the table?

....

....

....

....

....

....

....

....

3

We can use the table to help us write numbers as <u>binary numbers</u>.
E.g. 5 = 1 0 1, 13 = 1 1 0 1. More rows could be added to the table to help us write the numbers up to 31 as binary numbers.

Complete the table and use it to write the numbers as binary numbers.

16	8	4	2	1	
					= 22
					= 27
					= 28
					= 31

22 ....   27 ....

28 ....   31 ....

Show your thinking

This table can only record numbers up to 31 using the digits 0 and 1.
How could the table be changed so that numbers
<u>bigger than 31</u> can be recorded using the digits 0 and 1?
HINT: look at the pattern in the column headings.

....

....

....

....

....

4

Write the following as <u>binary numbers</u>. You might need to draw a table.

36 ....

60 ....

75 ....

5 An alternative to using 1s and 0s is to use a <u>shaded square</u> to represent <u>1</u> and an <u>unshaded square</u> to represent <u>0</u>.

You can create <u>binary monsters</u> from the patterns created. The monster below can be described using the code: 17, 21, 27, 14, 14, 10, 27

Complete the binary monster using the totals at the ends of the rows.

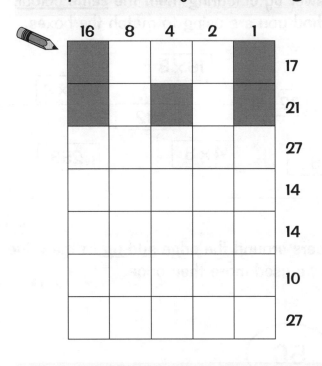

How lovely to meet you! What's your name?

6 You are going to create your own binary monster. First shade the squares to make your monster, then write the totals at the end of the rows.

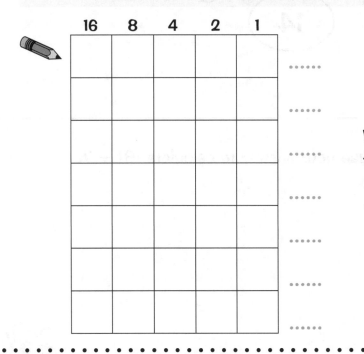

What is the binary code for your monster?

....

Take the binary code for your monster and <u>double</u> each number in it.
Redraw the monster on to a new grid (you may need to add a column).
What changes do you notice about the monster?

Now Try This

Section One — Calculations

Division and Doubling

Warm Up Question

Match each calculation with its answer by colouring them the <u>same colour</u>. Talk to your partner about the method you are using to match the boxes.

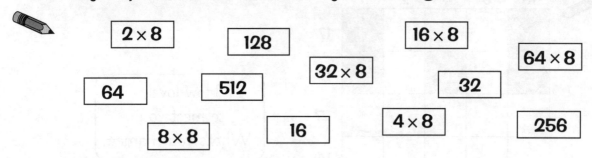

2×8	128		16×8	
		32×8		64×8
64	512		32	
8×8	16	4×8		256

1 With a partner, find which numbers around the edge <u>add up</u> to the value in the middle. Numbers cannot be used more than once.

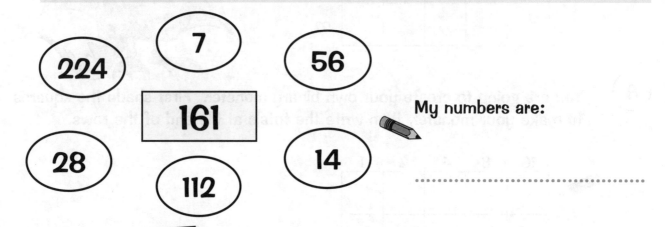

224   7   56

161

28   112   14

My numbers are:

....

Show your thinking

Think about how you can use your answer to calculate 161 ÷ 7.

Here's a bit of a hint: $7 \times 1 = 7$
$7 \times 2 = 14 \ldots$

2 Use the numbers below (as well as what you and your partner think is going on in Question 1) to calculate 342 ÷ 9.

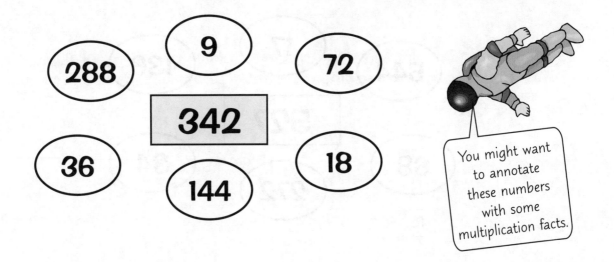

You might want to annotate these numbers with some multiplication facts.

342 ÷ 9 = ...

3 Now have a go at 473 ÷ 11.

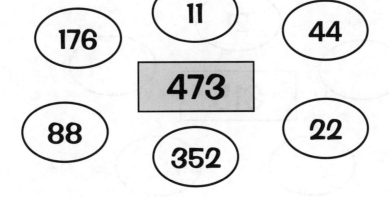

473 ÷ 11 = ...

Section One — Calculations

4 Yep, you're an expert now... See if you and your partner can use some of the numbers below to help you work out 527 ÷ 17.

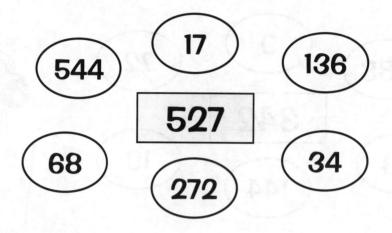

527 ÷ 17 = ...

5 There's some extra work to be done here to calculate 315 ÷ 21.

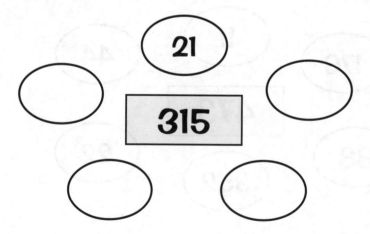

315 ÷ 21 = ...

Section One — Calculations

6 See if you and your partner can calculate 126 ÷ 4.5.

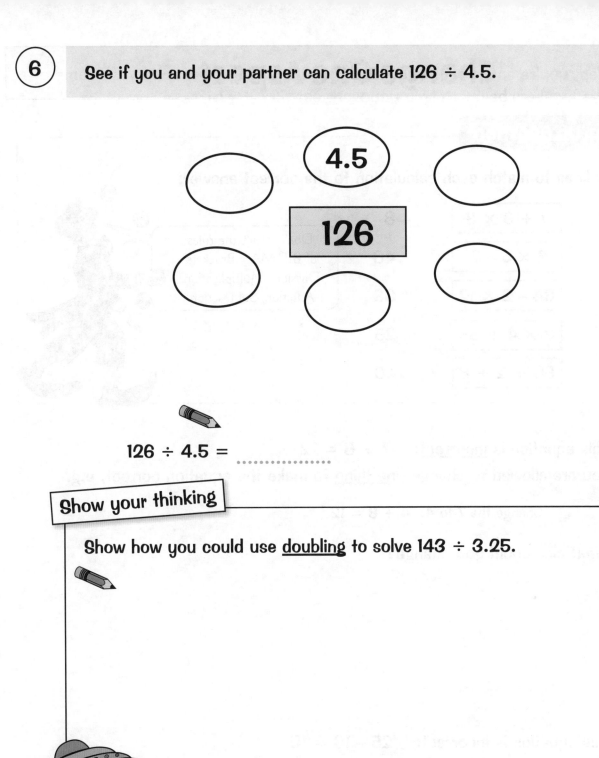

4.5

126

126 ÷ 4.5 = ...

Show your thinking

Show how you could use <u>doubling</u> to solve 143 ÷ 3.25.

 Now Try This Make up a division of your own for someone else to work out. Then swap with a partner.

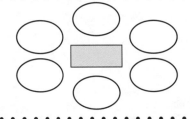

     Section One — Calculations

Change One Aspect

Draw lines to match each calculation to the correct answer:

$7 + 6 \times 3$	8
$3 \times 5 - 7$	48
$64 - 2 \times 12$	33
$3 \times 4 + 6^2$	25
$50 \div 2 + 8$	40

Don't forget the rules of BIDMAS: Brackets, Division, Multiplication, Addition, Subtraction.

1 This equation is <u>incorrect</u>: $7 + 8 = 12$

You are allowed to change <u>one thing</u> to make the equation correct, e.g.

Change the 7 to 4: $4 + 8 = 12$

What else could you change?

2 This equation is incorrect: $25 - 13 = 18$.
Change one thing to make it correct.

What else could you change?

3

Now you're going to look at a <u>two-step calculation</u> which is incorrect:

$$30 + 10 \times 2 = 10$$

Change <u>one number</u> in this equation to make it correct.

Now change a <u>different aspect</u>
of the equation (not a number)
to make it correct.

Remember
BIDMAS
in this one.

You could change
an operation (such
as multiplication to
division) or add brackets.

4

This equation is <u>incorrect</u>: $5 + 6 \times 3 - 8 = 25$
Change <u>different aspects</u> of the equation one at a time.
How many different aspects can you change to make the equation correct?

5 $7 + 2 \times 5 - 2 =$ a whole number between 11 and 20.

How many ways can you change one aspect of this equation so that it is still <u>true</u>? Write all the possibilities you can find below.

Remember to be systematic in your working.

Now Try This

Caleen Calculator says that by adding brackets to the calculation $7 + 3 \times 8 - 5$, she can create 4 different answers.

Do you agree with her? Explain your reasoning.

Multiplying Fractions

Warm Up Questions

Complete the sequences of fractions below by filling in the gaps:

a) $\frac{4}{7}$ $\frac{4}{14}$ .... $\frac{4}{28}$ ....

b) $\frac{1}{2}$ .... $\frac{3}{2}$ $\frac{4}{2}$ .... $\frac{6}{2}$

c) .... $1\frac{1}{5}$ $1\frac{3}{5}$ .... $2\frac{2}{5}$

d) $\frac{3}{5}$ $\frac{6}{5}$ $\frac{12}{5}$ $\frac{24}{5}$ ....

1 Work with a partner. You will each need a piece of A5 size paper (half of A4).

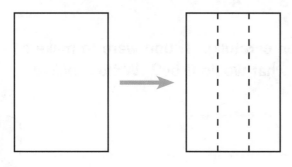

Fold your piece of paper into three **equal** width strips (thirds) as shown.

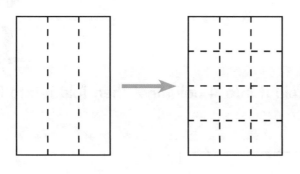

Now fold your paper into **quarters** as shown.

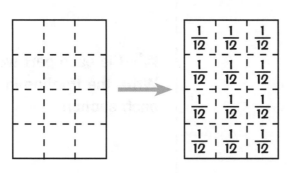

Do you agree that one part is **one twelfth** of the whole? Talk to your partner.

Write $\frac{1}{12}$ in each space.

2 Fold your piece of paper to show $\frac{3}{4}$ of 1 whole:

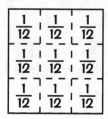

So $\frac{3}{4} = $ .....

Using your paper, what does one third of three quarters look like?
Draw it below:

So $\frac{1}{3}$ of $\frac{3}{4} = $ .....

This can also be written as $\frac{1}{3} \times \frac{3}{4} = $ .....

Look at the fraction calculation carefully. If you were to make a
rule for multiplying fractions, what would it be? Write it below.

3 With a new piece of paper, fold it into 4 columns, then fold it into 5 rows.
Draw what it looks like below.

What is each part worth?
Write the fraction in
each section.

Section Two — Fractions and Ratios

Using fifths (from 5 rows) and quarters (from 4 columns), use your paper to solve different multiplications of fractions, e.g. $\frac{1}{4}$ of $\frac{3}{5}$ or $\frac{2}{5}$ of $\frac{3}{4}$. Record your workings below.

It might help to fold your paper to show what each step looks like before writing the multiplication and its answer.

4 Repeat question 3 choosing any number of columns and rows (make sure you choose numbers you can fold the paper into). Show your workings and findings below. Try to find as many of the possible multiplications as you can.

Now Try This

Show two different methods of working out the following problem:
Rani scored 6 out of 8 in her last maths test. One quarter of her correct answers were for fraction questions. What fraction is this of the total number of questions in the test?

Section Two — Fractions and Ratios

Fractions to Decimals

1) Draw lines to match each fraction to its equivalent decimal.

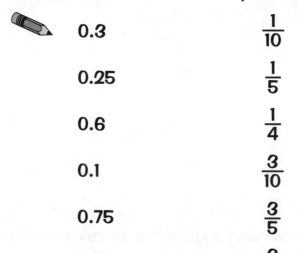

0.3	$\frac{1}{10}$
0.25	$\frac{1}{5}$
0.6	$\frac{1}{4}$
0.1	$\frac{3}{10}$
0.75	$\frac{3}{5}$
0.2	$\frac{3}{4}$

2) Put these decimal numbers in increasing order of size.

0.2   0.15   0.302   0.7   0.55   0.099

....

①

- Choose a fraction $\frac{a}{b}$ where both a and b are whole numbers less than or including 30.
- Perform the calculation on a calculator and write down the decimal answer.

E.g. fraction: $\frac{2}{9}$

$2 \div 9 = 0.\underline{22222222}...$

When a number after the decimal point is repeated forever like 0.222222..., it can be written 0.$\dot{2}$. This is called a recurring decimal.

Write your fraction and its equivalent decimal below.

If the number has a never-ending string of digits after the decimal point, write all the digits that your calculator shows, followed by '...', or use a dot to show a recurring decimal.

Fraction: ....   Decimal: ....

2 Repeat the steps of question 1 a few more times using different numerators and denominators each time.

Fraction	Decimal

3 Write each decimal you have on a separate piece of paper (big so everyone can see it). Share your decimals with others in the class.

- Does anyone have the same decimal number as you?
- What fraction did they use to create it?
- Are there others with the same decimal value who used a different fraction to create it?

Write your findings below.

What do your findings show?

....

....

....

....

Section Two — Fractions and Ratios

(4) Now use the table below to record decimals found by dividing the numerator of a fraction by its denominator.

NUMERATOR										
10							1.42 857i̇			
9	9									
8			2.6̇							
7										0.7
6				1.5						
5						0.83̇		0.625		
4					0.8					
3								0.375		
2			1						0.2̇	
1							0.i̇4 2857̇			
÷	1	2	3	4	5	6	7	8	9	10

DENOMINATOR

What patterns can you see in the table?

....

....

....

....

....

Section Two — Fractions and Ratios

5 Find decimal numbers in the table that are the same (you could shade them in the same colour). Record the decimals with their corresponding fractions below.

$$\text{E.g. }1.5 = \frac{6}{4}, \frac{3}{2}, \frac{9}{6}$$

Explore what happens when you create more fractions with a denominator of 9 and convert them into decimal numbers.

What happens when the denominator is 99?
Record your findings.

What do you think will happen when the denominator is 999?
Convert some numbers with a denominator of 999 into decimals.
Were you correct?

Section Two — Fractions and Ratios

Number Rod Ratios

This shows the ratio 1 : 2 because there is 1 circle and 2 triangles.

Use circles and triangles to show each ratio.

1 : 3	2 : 3	1 : 4	3 : 5

① In return for your help battling a troll, a leprechaun has decided to split his pot of gold with you.
He is going to keep <u>more</u> of the gold for <u>himself</u>, but will let you choose the ratio in which the gold is split.

You're going to use number rods to find possible ratios (with numbers up to 6) in which the gold could be split.

E.g. a white rod (length 1) and a red rod (length 2) can be used to show the ratio: 1 : 2.

The gold has been split into 3 equal parts. You'll get 1 of these parts and the leprechaun will keep 2 parts.

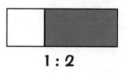

1 : 2

What ratio can you represent using these number rods?

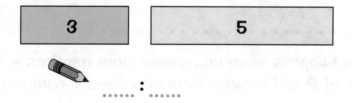

.... : ....

How many parts is the gold split into this time? ....

How many of these parts will you get? ....

How many of these parts will the leprechaun keep? ....

2

Make sure you and your partner have these number rods:

1	2	3	4

5	6

Find all the different <u>ratios</u> that the gold could be split in using these numbers.

Show your thinking

How did you make sure that you found <u>all</u> the possible ratios?

Section Two — Fractions and Ratios

3 Looking at the ratios <u>3:5</u> and <u>1:2</u>, which ratio would give you more of the leprechaun's gold? Show your working below.

You might find it helpful to use counters to represent the pieces of gold.

④ In Question 2, you found all the possible ratios using these rods.

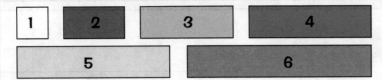

Show which ratio will give you the **most gold**.

 Now Try This

Just as you've worked out the best ratio, the leprechaun's <u>twin brother</u> arrives and says he wants a share too. The first leprechaun will still get <u>more than you</u>, but his twin brother will get <u>less than you</u>.

Using the rods from this page, which ratio should the gold be divided into so that you get the <u>largest</u> amount possible?

Following the same rules, which ratio would the leprechaun's twin want the gold to be split into?

Section Three — Geometry

Four Quadrants

1) What are the coordinates for each of the crosses?

   A (...... , ...)   C (...... , ...)

   B (...... , ...)   D (...... , ...)

2) If each cross was translated 2 squares left and 1 square down, what would its new coordinates be?

   A (...... , ...)   C (...... , ...)

   B (...... , ...)   D (...... , ...)

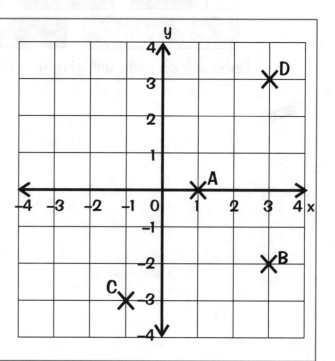

1 Plot and label these points on the axes below:
$A_i(2, 1)$, $B_i(4, 2)$, $C_i(4, 3)$, $D_i(2, 3)$. Join the points to form a shape.

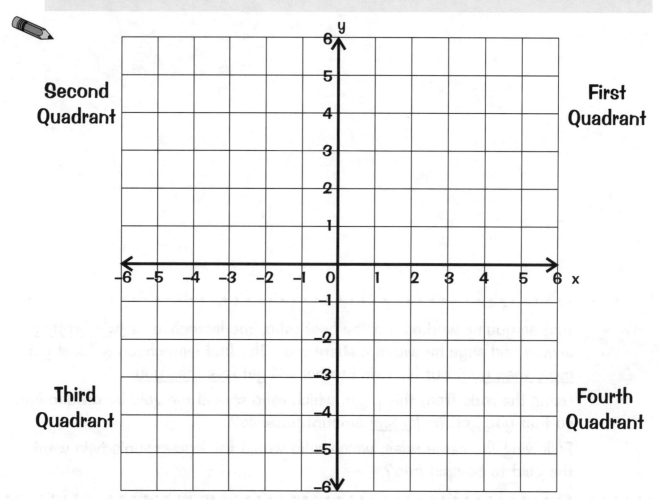

Second Quadrant   First Quadrant

Third Quadrant   Fourth Quadrant

2 Now <u>reverse</u> each pair of coordinates so $A_1(2, 1)$ changes to $A_2(1, 2)$, and so on. Write the new coordinates below.

$A_2($......, ...$)$ $B_2($......, ...$)$ $C_2($......, ...$)$ $D_2($......, ...$)$

Plot and label the points on the grid. Join them to form a second shape. Describe the <u>transformation</u> that maps the first shape onto the second.

....

....

....

> Think about whether the shape has been reflected across a line or translated ('slid') around the grid.

3 You're going to change the coordinates $A_1(2, 1)$, $B_1(4, 2)$, $C_1(4, 3)$ and $D_1(2, 3)$ again. This time, make each x-value <u>negative</u> and keep each y-value <u>the same</u>. Write the new coordinates below.

$A_3($......, ...$)$ $B_3($......, ...$)$

$C_3($......, ...$)$ $D_3($......, ...$)$

Plot and label the points on the grid. Join them to make a third shape. Describe the transformation that maps the first shape onto the third.

....

....

....

> When you describe a reflection, you need to say what line a shape has been reflected in — it'll often be the x- or y-axis.

Section Three — Geometry

4 Using the coordinates $A_1(2, 1)$, $B_1(4, 2)$, $C_1(4, 3)$ and $D_1(2, 3)$ again, keep each x-value <u>the same</u> and make each y-value <u>negative</u>. Write the new coordinates below.

$A_4(\ldots, \ldots)$ $B_4(\ldots, \ldots)$ $C_4(\ldots, \ldots)$ $D_4(\ldots, \ldots)$

Plot and label the points on the grid. Join them to make a fourth shape. Describe the transformation that maps the first shape onto the fourth.

....

....

....

5 What do you think will happen to the first shape if you make <u>both</u> the x- and y-values of its coordinates <u>negative</u>? Write your prediction.

....

....

....

6 Now you're going to test your prediction. First make both the x- and y-values of the coordinates $A_1(2, 1)$, $B_1(4, 2)$, $C_1(4, 3)$, $D_1(2, 3)$ <u>negative</u>. Then plot and join the coordinates on the same grid as the other shapes.

$A_5(\ldots, \ldots)$ $B_5(\ldots, \ldots)$ $C_5(\ldots, \ldots)$ $D_5(\ldots, \ldots)$

Was your prediction correct? If not, what happened to the shape?

....

....

Section Three — Geometry

7 On the grid below, plot points $A_1(2, 1)$, $B_1(4, 2)$, $C_1(4, 3)$ and $D_1(2, 3)$ again. Then <u>subtract 4</u> from each x-value and <u>subtract 5</u> from each y-value. Write the new coordinates below and plot them on the grid.

$A_6($......, ...$)$

$B_6($......, ...$)$

$C_6($......, ...$)$

$D_6($......, ...$)$

Describe what has happened to the shape.

....

....

....

Now Try This For this activity, you will need a grid showing all 4 quadrants. With a partner, plot a shape and label it 1. Make up a <u>rule</u> that changes the x- or y-value (or both) of each point. Apply the rule and draw the new shape. Label it 2. Now swap with another pair in your class, and see if you can work out the rule they used to transform their shape.

Section Three — Geometry

Algebraic Shapes

Work out what the letters represent in each of these equations:

a) $7 + u = 56$ u = ...

b) $45 \div v = 5$ v = ...

c) $w - 7 = -15$ w = ...

d) $12 \times x = 4800$ x = ...

e) $y + 0.5 = 0.8$ y = ...

f) $z \div 6 = 0.5$ z = ...

1 Each letter represents a different length side of a triangle. Sides can be short (a), medium (b) or long (c). Use different combinations of lengths to make as many different triangles as you can.

Record your work like this:

You <u>don't</u> need to measure the lines — just think of **c** as about twice the length of **a**, and **b** is in between.

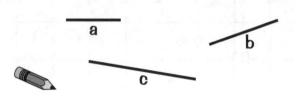

I found .... triangles in total.

2 You have two copies of the triangle below. The two triangles can be joined together, but the two sides that are joined together must be the same length and must completely join from corner to corner. You cannot reflect the triangle.

How many different shapes can you make? Draw them below and name the shapes you have created.

Be precise with your names.

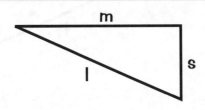

3 If the lengths are labelled s (for shortest side), m (for middle length) and l (for longest side), the <u>perimeter</u> of one triangle is s + m + l.

Look at the shapes you made in Question 2. Write the equations for their perimeters.

4 Now you'll be joining <u>three</u> of the triangles together by sides of the same length, following the same rules as in question 2.
How many different trapeziums can you make?
What is the perimeter equation for each of them?

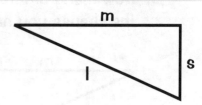

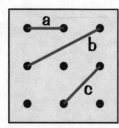 On a pegboard, create quadrilaterals using an elastic band. Use the coding a, b and c to work out the lengths of each side.
Calculate the perimeter of each of the quadrilaterals you create.
Record your measurements like this: $\longrightarrow$ 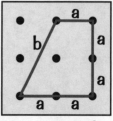 $P = 5a + b$

Section Three — Geometry

Volume and Surface Area

Find 3 numbers that multiply to make the products below, e.g. 16 = 2 × 2 × 4.

a) 6 = ... × .... × ....

b) 15 = ... × .... × ....

c) 20 = ... × .... × ....

d) 24 = ... × .... × ....

e) 36 = ... × .... × ....

1

Use only the following numbers to find __four__ groups of 3 numbers that multiply to make __12__.

1   1   1   1   2   2   2   3   3   4   6   12

.... × .... × .... = 12   .... × .... × .... = 12

.... × .... × .... = 12   .... × .... × .... = 12

2

Using the groups of 3 numbers in question 1 as dimensions, make 4 __cuboids__ using connecting cubes.

E.g. this cuboid has these dimensions:
2 × 2 × 4 = 16 cm³

Did you know the '3'
of cm³ is there to show
there are 3 dimensions —
length, width and height?

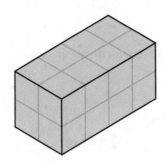

Section Three — Geometry

3 The image below shows how to draw a 3-dimensional shape using <u>isometric</u> dotty paper. Practise drawing some cubes of your own.

Now, use the isometric dotty paper below to draw images of the cuboids you created in question 2. Label the lengths of the edges.

Section Three — Geometry

4 You can calculate the <u>surface area</u> of a cuboid as shown below.

1 cm
1 cm
12 cm

Area of 1 rectangle = 12 × 1 = 12 cm²

The cuboid has **4** of these rectangular faces, so area of 4 rectangles = 12 cm² × 4 = **48 cm²**

Area of 1 square = 1 × 1 = 1 cm²

The cuboid has **2** of these square faces, so area of 2 squares = 1 cm² × 2 = **2 cm²**

Total surface area =
48 cm² + 2 cm² = <u>50 cm²</u>

 Of the other three cuboids with the volume 12 cm³, which do you think will have the largest surface area and why? Write your thoughts below.

....

....

....

Using the method at the top of the page, calculate the total surface area of the three other cuboids with volume 12 cm³.

.... cm²   .... cm²   .... cm²

 Repeat Questions 1-4 with a different volume. You can choose from 20 cm³, 24 cm³ or 36 cm³.

HINT: 20 cm³ has 4 different possible cuboids, 24 cm³ has 6, and 36 cm³ has 8.

 ✓   ✓   ✓

How Old Am I?

Warm Up Questions

Warm Up Questions

How many days are there in each month of the year?

January: ....   May: ....   September: ....

February: ....   June: ....   October: ....

March: ....   July: ....   November: ....

April: ....   August: ....   December: ....

How is February different from the other months?

....

....

1 On what date were you born? Calculate exactly how old you are in <u>years</u>, <u>months</u> and <u>days</u>.

I am .... years, ... months and .... days old.

2 Now use your workings from question 1 to calculate how old you are in <u>months</u>, to the nearest month.

I am .... months old.

3 Next, work out how many <u>days</u> old you are.
(Don't forget about leap years!)

The year 2012 was a leap year — they happen every 4 years.

I am .... days old.

4 Using your answer to question 3, work out how old are you in <u>weeks</u>, to the nearest week.

I am .... weeks old.

Section Four — Measurement and Statistics

5

1 day = 24 hours   1 hour = 60 minutes

Using this knowledge, calculate the answers to the following questions.

If you don't know what time you were born at, imagine you were born at exactly <u>1 o'clock</u> in the <u>afternoon</u>.

How old are you in <u>hours</u>, to the nearest hour?

Don't forget to include how many hours have passed today, and how many hours passed after your birth on the day you were born.

I am .... hours old.

How old are you in <u>minutes</u>, to the nearest minute?

The challenge with finding how many minutes old you are is that your answer will keep changing as you calculate it.

The good news is you're allowed to use a calculator!

I am .... minutes old.

Now Try This

Work with a group. Write the age in minutes that you calculated onto a piece of paper. Take turns in reading them out, then get yourself into order from youngest to oldest. What is your total age in minutes?

By how many minutes is the oldest person older than the youngest person?

Section Four — Measurement and Statistics

Stars and Statistics

Warm Up Questions

The <u>mean</u> (average) is found by <u>adding</u> all the numbers in a group and <u>dividing</u> by how many numbers there are. Find the mean of the numbers in each circle:

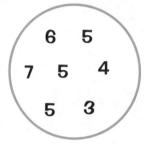

6 5

7 5 4

5 3

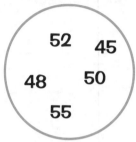

10

14 10 12

12 11

16

19

52 45

48 50

55

.... ÷ .... = ... ÷ .... = ... ÷ .... = ...

---

1 Your teacher will show you an image of some stars for about **5 seconds**.
How many stars do you think you saw?
Write your <u>estimate</u> in the star below.

Your teacher will now collect together all the estimates from the class. <u>Record</u> them all in the space below.

Think about how you could be systematic in recording the estimates. E.g. you might put them in order.

---

2 Find the <u>range</u> of the estimates. The range is the <u>difference</u> between the <u>minimum</u> and <u>maximum</u> values.

Section Four — Measurement and Statistics

(3) How could you work out a <u>class estimate</u> for the number of stars?

Show your thinking

Discuss your ideas with a partner and write them below.

(4) You are now going to find the <u>mode</u>, <u>median</u> and <u>mean</u> for the estimates.
The mode is the value that the largest number of people said.
The median is the middle value when you put all the numbers in order.

Mode

Median

The MOde is the MOst popular.

The MEDian is like the MEDium. It might fall halfway between two values.

Mean

Hmm... so many numbers...
You may need to use a calculator.

The mean might not be a whole number.

Section Four — Measurement and Statistics

Show your thinking

Do you think the mean, mode or median is the <u>best class estimate</u>? Explain why.

5 Now you know the class averages, you might want to change your estimate. Write your <u>new estimate</u> in the star.

Your teacher will now collect together all the new estimates from the class.
Record them all in the space below.

6 Find the <u>range</u> of the new estimates.

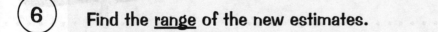

Section Four — Measurement and Statistics

44

Show your thinking

Is the range of this set of estimates different from the range of the first set of estimates? Why do you think this is?

7 Now find the <u>mode</u>, <u>median</u> and <u>mean</u> for the new estimates.

Mode

Median

Mean

8 Your teacher will now reveal how many stars there really were.

Write down the difference between the number of real stars and the estimate you wrote in Question 5.

A set of <u>5 values</u> has a mode of 6, a median of 6 and a mean of 7. Suggest what the values might be. Can you think of any <u>different</u> answers?

Section Four — Measurement and Statistics

Answers

Section One – Calculations
Pages 3-5 – Always, Sometimes or Never?

Warm Up: E.g. (if the calculator works them out in given order rather than using BIDMAS): $3 - 2 = \textbf{1}$; **2**; **3**; $7 - 3 = \textbf{4}$; $7 - 2 = \textbf{5}$; $2 \times 3 = \textbf{6}$; **7**; $7 - 3 = 4, \times 2 = \textbf{8}$; $3 \times 3 = \textbf{9}$; $7 - 2 = 5, \times 2 = \textbf{10}$; $2 \times 7 - 3 = \textbf{11}$; $2 \times 3 \times 2 = \textbf{12}$; $7 - 3 = 4, \times 2 \times 2 = 16, - 3 = \textbf{13}$; $2 \times 7 = \textbf{14}$; $3 \times 7 - 3 - 3 = \textbf{15}$; $3 \times 7 - 3 - 2 = \textbf{16}$; $3 \times 7 - 2 - 2 = \textbf{17}$; $2 \times 3 \times 3 = \textbf{18}$; $3 \times 7 - 2 = \textbf{19}$; $7 - 2 = 5, \times 2 \times 2 = \textbf{20}$

Investigation

1) E.g. it is always true because multiplying a number means you have more lots of it. OR
   It is sometimes true because when you multiply a number by something like 5 or 7, the result is higher. But when you multiply it by a decimal like 0.1 or 0.2, the result is lower.

2) a) 0.5; b) 0.2; c) 0.4; d) 0.1; e) 0.4;
   f) –2; g) –3; h) –0.3; i) 0.5; j) 0.1
   Show your thinking: E.g. multiplying by a decimal number less than 1 makes the answer lower, e.g. $6 \times 0.5 = 3$.
   When the number is positive, multiplying by a negative number also makes the answer lower, e.g. $6 \times -5 = -30$.

3) E.g. $0.2 \times 0.1 = 0.02$; $0.3 \times 0.4 = 0.12$;
   $0.4 \times 0.4 = 0.16$; $0.2 \times 0.2 = 0.04$ etc.

Now Try This
E.g. $10 \times 2 = 40 \times 0.5$; $10 \times 0.3 = 6 \times 0.5$; $10 \times -4 = -80 \times 0.5$

Pages 6-9 – Binary Numbers

Warm Up
1) $8 + 1$; 2) $8 + 4 + 2$; 3) $16 + 4 + 1$

Investigation
1)
1: 1	12: 8 + 4	22: 16 + 4 + 2
2: 2	13: 8 + 4 + 1	23: 16 + 4 + 2 + 1
3: 2 + 1	14: 8 + 4 + 2	24: 16 + 8
4: 4	15: 8 + 4 + 2 + 1	25: 16 + 8 + 1
5: 4 + 1	16: 16	26: 16 + 8 + 2
6: 4 + 2	17: 16 + 1	27: 16 + 8 + 2 + 1
7: 4 + 2 + 1	18: 16 + 2	28: 16 + 8 + 4
8: 8	19: 16 + 2 + 1	29: 16 + 8 + 4 + 1
9: 8 + 1	20: 16 + 4	30: 16 + 8 + 4 + 2
10: 8 + 2	21: 16 + 4 + 1	31: 16 + 8 + 4
11: 8 + 2 + 1		+ 2 + 1

2)
$110 = 6$ $1100 = 12$
$111 = 7$ $1101 = 13$
$1000 = 8$ $1110 = 14$
$1001 = 9$ $1111 = 15$
$1010 = 10$ $10000 = 16$
$1011 = 11$

E.g. odd numbers end in 1 and even numbers end in 0. In the column with 2 as its heading, the pattern goes 1 1 0 0 1 1 0 0. In the column with 4 as its heading, the pattern goes 1 1 1 1 0 0 0 0 1 1 1 1.

3) $22 = 10110$ $27 = 11011$
   $28 = 11100$ $31 = 11111$
   Extra columns should be added on the left.
   Each column heading is double the one to the right of it, so the heading of the next column should be 32 (16 × 2), then the next 64 (32 × 2).

4) $36 = 100100$ $60 = 111100$ $75 = 1001011$

5)

6) E.g. 4, 14, 4, 31, 4, 14, 17:

Now Try This
E.g. doubled binary code = 8, 28, 8, 62, 8, 28, 34:
The monster has not changed in size or shape, but it has moved one column to the left.

Pages 10-13 – Division and Doubling

Warm Up: $2 \times 8 = 16$; $16 \times 8 = 128$; $8 \times 8 = 64$; $64 \times 8 = 512$; $32 \times 8 = 256$; $4 \times 8 = 32$

Investigation
1) My numbers are: 7, 14, 28, 112.
   Add together how many 'lots of 7' are needed to make each of these numbers: $1 + 2 + 4 + 16 = 23$, so $161 \div 7 = \textbf{23}$.
2) 38   3) 43   4) 31   5) 15
6) 28 $143 \div 3.25 = 44$

Pages 14-16 – Change One Aspect

Warm Up
$7 + 6 \times 3 = 25$; $3 \times 5 - 7 = 8$; $64 - 2 \times 12 = 40$;
$3 \times 4 + 6^2 = 48$; $50 \div 2 + 8 = 33$

Investigation
1) E.g. change the 8 to 5: $7 + 5 = 12$.
2) Change the 25 to 31: $31 - 13 = 18$ / change the 13 to 7: $25 - 7 = 18$ / change the 18 to 12: $25 - 13 = 12$.
3) E.g. change the 10 to 50: $30 + 10 \times 2 = 30 + 20 = 50$.
   Change the + to –: $30 - 10 \times 2 = 30 - 20 = 10$.
4) E.g. Change 5 to 15: $15 + 6 \times 3 - 8 = 25$ ✓
   Change 3 to 5: $5 + 6 \times 5 - 8 = 27$ ✗
   Change 6 to 9: $5 + 9 \times 3 - 8 = 24$ ✗
   Change 25 to 15: $5 + 6 \times 3 - 8 = 15$ ✓
   Change + to –: $5 - 6 \times 3 - 8 = -21$ ✗
   Change × to ÷: $5 + 6 \div 3 - 8 = -1$ ✗
   Change – to +: $5 + 6 \times 3 + 8 = 31$ ✗
   Add brackets around the addition:
   $(5 + 6) \times 3 - 8 = 25$ ✓
   Add brackets around the subtraction:
   $5 + 6 \times (3 - 8) = -25$ ✗
5)
$7 + 2 \times 5 - 2 = 15$	$9 + 2 \times 5 - 2 = 17$	$7 + 2 \times 5 - 0 = 17$
$7 + 2 \times (5 - 2) = 13$	$10 + 2 \times 5 - 2 = 18$	$7 + 2 \times 5 - 1 = 16$
$7 + 2 + 5 - 2 = 12$	$11 + 2 \times 5 - 2 = 19$	$7 + 2 \times 5 - 3 = 14$
$7 + 2 \times 5 + 2 = 19$	$12 + 2 \times 5 - 2 = 20$	$7 + 2 \times 5 - 4 = 13$
$7 + 2 \times 5 \div 2 = 12$	$7 + 3 \times 5 - 2 = 20$	$7 + 2 \times 5 - 5 = 12$
$3 + 2 \times 5 - 2 = 11$	$7 + 2 \times 3 - 2 = 11$	$7 + 2 \times 5 - 6 = 11$
$4 + 2 \times 5 - 2 = 12$	$7 + 2 \times 4 - 2 = 13$	$7 + 2 \times 5 - -1 = 18$
$5 + 2 \times 5 - 2 = 13$	$7 + 2 \times 6 - 2 = 17$	$7 + 2 \times 5 - -2 = 19$
$6 + 2 \times 5 - 2 = 14$	$7 + 2 \times 7 - 2 = 19$	$7 + 2 \times 5 - -3 = 20$
$8 + 2 \times 5 - 2 = 16$		

Now Try This
Caleen Calculator is correct. Brackets at the start: $(7 + 3) \times 8 - 5 = 75$. Brackets in the middle: $7 + (3 \times 8) - 5 = 26$. Brackets at the end: $7 + 3 \times (8 - 5) = 16$. 2 pairs of brackets: $(7 + 3) \times (8 - 5) = 30$.

Section Two – Fractions and Ratios
Pages 17-19 – Multiplying Fractions

Warm Up
a) $\dfrac{4}{21}$, $\dfrac{4}{35}$ b) $\dfrac{2}{2}$, $\dfrac{5}{2}$ c) $\dfrac{4}{5}$, 2   d) $\dfrac{24}{5}$, $\dfrac{48}{5}$

Investigation
2) $\dfrac{9}{12}$ $\boxed{\dfrac{1}{12} \mid \dfrac{1}{12} \mid \dfrac{1}{12}}$ $\dfrac{1}{3} \times \dfrac{3}{4} = \dfrac{3}{12}$ (or $\dfrac{1}{4}$)
   Multiply the numerators together and then multiply the denominators together.
3) E.g.
   $\dfrac{3}{5}$ of whole $\dfrac{1}{4} \times \dfrac{3}{5} = \dfrac{3}{20}$
4) Answers will vary.

Now Try This
E.g.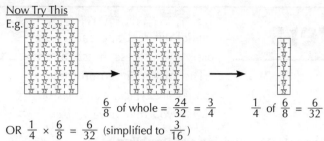

$$\frac{6}{8} \text{ of whole} = \frac{24}{32} = \frac{3}{4} \qquad \frac{1}{4} \text{ of } \frac{6}{8} = \frac{6}{32}$$

OR $\frac{1}{4} \times \frac{6}{8} = \frac{6}{32}$ (simplified to $\frac{3}{16}$)

Pages 20-23 – Fractions to Decimals

Warm Up
1) $0.3 = \frac{3}{10}$; $0.25 = \frac{1}{4}$; $0.6 = \frac{3}{5}$; $0.1 = \frac{1}{10}$; $0.75 = \frac{3}{4}$;
$0.2 = \frac{1}{5}$

2) 0.099, 0.15, 0.2, 0.302, 0.55, 0.7

Investigation
1) E.g. $\frac{3}{17} = 0.176470588...$
2) Answers will vary.
3) E.g. 0.4 could have come from the following:
$\frac{2}{5}, \frac{4}{10}, \frac{6}{15}, \frac{8}{20}, \frac{10}{25}, \frac{12}{30}$.
E.g. 0.4 means 4 tenths but from looking at calculations you can see that $\frac{4}{10}$ is equal to $\frac{8}{20}$. Because 0.4 is also made from $\frac{6}{15}, \frac{2}{5}, \frac{10}{25}$ and $\frac{12}{30}$, you can also see that $\frac{4}{10}$ is equal to these fractions too.

4)

÷	1	2	3	4	5	6	7	8	9	10
10	10	5	$3.\dot{3}$	2.5	2	$1.\dot{6}$	$1.\dot{4}2\dot{8}57\dot{1}$	1.25	$1.\dot{1}$	1
9	9	4.5	3	2.25	1.8	1.5	$1.\dot{2}85\dot{7}14$	1.125	1	0.9
8	8	4	$2.\dot{6}$	2	1.6	$1.\dot{3}$	$1.\dot{1}42\dot{8}57$	1	$0.\dot{8}$	0.8
7	7	3.5	$2.\dot{3}$	1.75	1.4	$1.1\dot{6}$	1	0.875	$0.\dot{7}$	0.7
6	6	3	2	1.5	1.2	1	$0.\dot{8}57\dot{1}42$	0.75	0.6	0.6
5	5	2.5	$1.\dot{6}$	1.25	1	$0.8\dot{3}$	$0.\dot{7}14\dot{2}85$	0.625	$0.\dot{5}$	0.5
4	4	2	$1.\dot{3}$	1	0.8	$0.\dot{6}$	$0.\dot{5}71\dot{4}28$	0.5	$0.\dot{4}$	0.4
3	3	1.5	1	0.75	0.6	0.5	$0.\dot{4}28\dot{5}71$	0.375	$0.\dot{3}$	0.3
2	2	1	$0.\dot{6}$	0.5	0.4	$0.\dot{3}$	$0.\dot{2}85\dot{7}14$	0.25	$0.\dot{2}$	0.2
1	1	0.5	$0.\dot{3}$	0.25	0.2	$0.1\dot{6}$	$0.\dot{1}42\dot{8}57$	0.125	$0.\dot{1}$	0.1

E.g. The recurring decimals only occur in numbers where the denominator is 7 or a multiple of 3.
5) Answers will vary, but should be taken from the table.
Now Try This: E.g. Fractions with a denominator of 9 always have a recurring decimal (except when it's a whole number). Fractions with a denominator of 99 have 2 alternating recurring digits. I predict that, for 999, they will have 3 alternating recurring digits.

Pages 24-27 – Number Rod Ratios

Warm Up
1:3   2:3   1:4   3:5
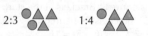

Investigation
1) 3:5; 8; 3; 5
2) 1:2, 1:3, 1:4, 1:5, 1:6, 2:3, 2:4, 2:5, 2:6, 3:4, 3:5, 3:6, 4:5, 4:6, 5:6
E.g. First we made all the ratios beginning with a 1, and we put them so that the other number was increasing in size. Then we made all the ratios beginning with a 2, and so on.
3) 3:5
4) 5:6

Now Try This
To give me the largest amount possible, the twin brother must get the smallest share possible. So the gold must be split in the ratio 5 : 6 : 1 (where I'll get 5 parts). The twin brother would want a large share, but it must still be smaller than the other two shares, so it will be 5 : 6 : 4 (where he'll get 4 parts).

Section Three – Geometry
Pages 28-31 – Four Quadrants

Warm Up
1) A (1, 0)   B (3, –2),   C (–1, –3)   D (3, 3)
2) A (–1, –1)   B (1, –3)   C (–3, –4)   D (1, 2)

Investigation
1-6)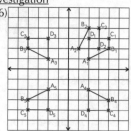

2) A_2(1, 2) B_2(2, 4) C_2(3, 4) D_2(3, 2)
A reflection in a diagonal line running from bottom left to top right.
3) A_3(–2, 1) B_3(–4, 2) C_3(–4, 3) D_3(–2, 3)
A reflection in the y-axis.
4) A_4(2, –1) B_4(4, –2) C_4(4, –3) D_4(2, –3)
A reflection in the x-axis.
5) E.g. It will move into the third quadrant. It will be reflected in the x- and y-axes.
6) A_5(–2, –1) B_5(–4, –2) C_5(–4, –3) D_5(–2, –3)
7) A_6(–2, –4) B_6(0, –3) C_6(0, –2) D_6(–2, –2)
It has moved 4 squares left and 5 squares down.
It is still the same way up and the same way round.
Now Try This: Many possible answers.

Pages 32-34 – Algebraic Shapes
Warm Up: a) 49   b) 9   c) –8   d) 400   e) 0.3   f) 3
Investigation
1) Up to 10 triangles will have been found.
2) Joining sides s together gives a parallelogram. Joining sides l gives a rectangle. Joining sides m gives a parallelogram.
3) Parallelogram with sides s joined together =
m + l + m + l = 2m + 2l
Rectangle = s + m + s + m = 2s + 2m
Parallelogram with sides m joined together =
s + l + s + l = 2s + 2l
4) 3 trapeziums. Perimeters: 3m + s + l, 3s + l + m and 3l + m + s
Now Try This: 15 possible shapes (not including shape in question)

Pages 35-37 – Volume and Surface Area
Warm Up E.g.:
a) $1 \times 2 \times 3$ b) $1 \times 3 \times 5$ c) $2 \times 2 \times 5$ d) $2 \times 3 \times 4$
e) $3 \times 3 \times 4$
Investigation
1) $1 \times 1 \times 12 = 12$, $1 \times 2 \times 6 = 12$, $1 \times 3 \times 4 = 12$, $2 \times 2 \times 3 = 12$
3)
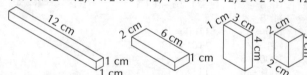
4) E.g. the cuboid with dimensions $1 \times 2 \times 6$, because it looks like it has the highest number of exposed sides of individual cubes.
$1 \times 2 \times 6$: 40 cm², $1 \times 3 \times 4$: 38 cm², $2 \times 2 \times 3$: 32 cm²

Section Four – Measurement and Statistics
Pages 38-40 – How Old Am I?
Warm Up: 31, 28 or 29, 31, 30, 31, 30, 31, 31, 30 , 31, 30 , 31
February usually has 28 days, but every 4 years it has 29 days.
Investigation: Answers will vary depending on age.
2) E.g. on your 11th birthday, you're 132 months old.
3) E.g. on your 11th birthday, you're 574 weeks old.
4) E.g. on your 11th birthday, you're about 4017 days old, but it depends on how many leap years you've lived through.
5) Your answer should be in the high tens of thousands or over 100 000 for hours, and will reach into the millions for minutes.
Now Try This: Answers will vary.

Pages 41-44 – Stars and Statistics
Warm Up: 5, 13, 50
Investigation: Answers based on estimates will vary.
3) E.g. we could find the mean by adding all the estimates and dividing the total by the number of children in the class.
6) E.g. the range was smaller in the second set because people who had originally made very high or low estimates changed them.
The real number of stars is 32.
Now Try This: Many possible answers, e.g. 1, 6, 6, 6, 16.

Answers